YOU'RE THE VO[ICE]
Sammy Davis Jnr.

IMP

International MUSIC Publications

© International Music Publications Limited
Griffin House 161 Hammersmith Road London W6 8BS England

Editorial, arranging, engraving and recording Artemis Music Limited (www.artemismusic.com)
Design: IMP Studio
Photography: David Redfern / Redferns Music Picture Library

Published 2004

International
MUSIC
Publications

© International Music Publications Limited
Griffin House 161 Hammersmith Road London W6 8BS England

Sammy Davis Jnr.
Born 8th December 1925
Died 16th May 1990

Sammy Davis Jnr.; an entertainment phenomenon. You name it – singing, dancing, acting – he could, or would attempt to, do it. In his lifetime he made 40 albums and appeared in countless films and television programmes, becoming one of the most familiar faces of the 1950s through to the 1980s.

The son of New York vaudeville star Sammy Davis and Elvera Sanchez, a Puerto Rican dancer, Sammy Jnr. was brought up by his father from the age of two and had starred in his first film at six. After receiving dance coaching from Bill 'Bojangles' Robinson, Davis joined the Will Mastin Trio alongside his father and adopted uncle, and it was whilst appearing with the trio as an opener for Frank Sinatra in New York, that Davis and Sinatra struck up what was to be a life-long friendship.

Having worked with such legendary names as Bob Hope, Jack Benny and Mickey Rooney, Davis signed for Decca Records in 1954 and released his first album, *Starring Sammy Davis Jnr.*, which stayed at No.1 for six weeks. In the same year he was involved in a near-fatal car crash whilst returning to Los Angeles, as a result of which he lost his left eye. Whilst recovering, he converted to Judaism and then courted social controversy during a number of inter-racial romances, eventually marrying Swedish actress May Britt in 1960.

Around the same time he appeared in a series of films (including *Ocean's Eleven*) with his Rat Pack colleagues and became associated with the civil rights movement, working with the likes of Martin Luther King. Throughout the 1970s and 80s he made frequent appearances in Las Vegas and in 1988 began a Rat Pack concert tour with Frank Sinatra and Dean Martin, during which he showed signs of the illness which led to him announcing in September 1989 that he had throat cancer. He eventually died of the disease at his Beverly Hills home in May of the following year.

"Real success is not on the stage, but off the stage as a human being, and how you get along with your fellow man."

For Once In My Life

Words by Ronald Miller
Music by Orlando Murden

Backing

Boogaloo tempo

For

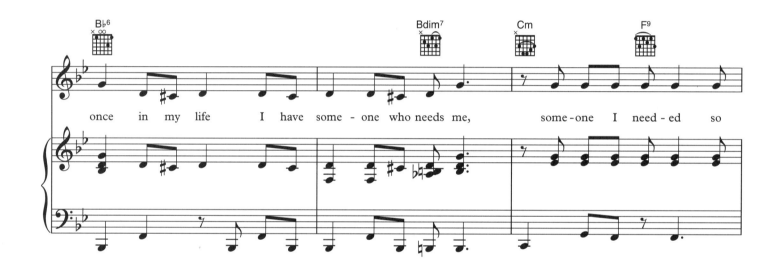

once in my life I have some-one who needs me, some-one I need-ed so

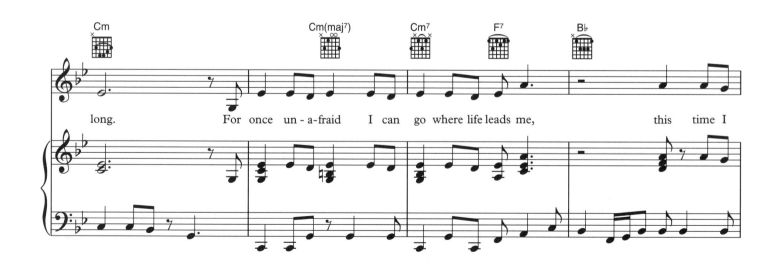

long. For once un-a-fraid I can go where life leads me, this time I

know I'm gon-na make it. For once in my life I got some-one who needs

me. For

once in my life I got some-one who needs___ me.

Hey There

Words and Music by Richard Adler and Jerry Ross

Backing

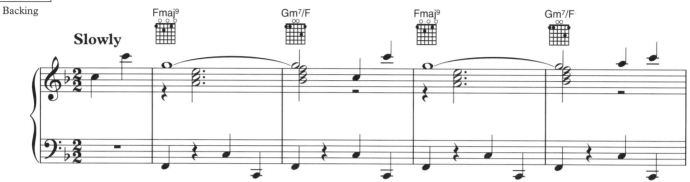

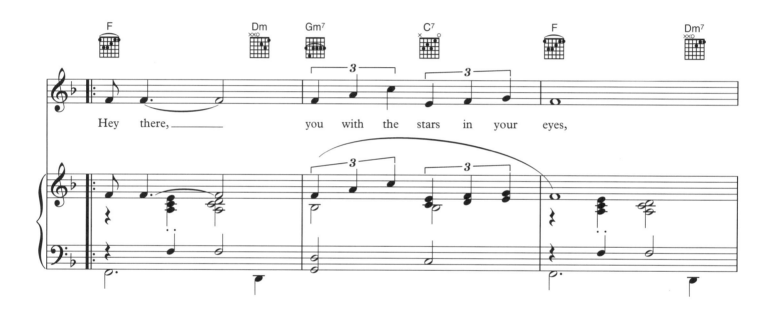

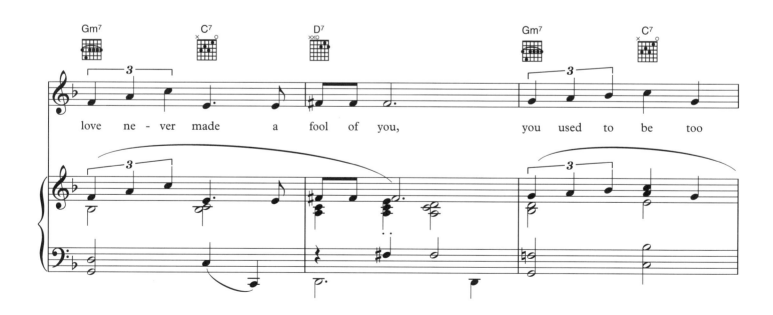

It's All Right With Me

Backing

Words and Music by Cole Porter

Slowly

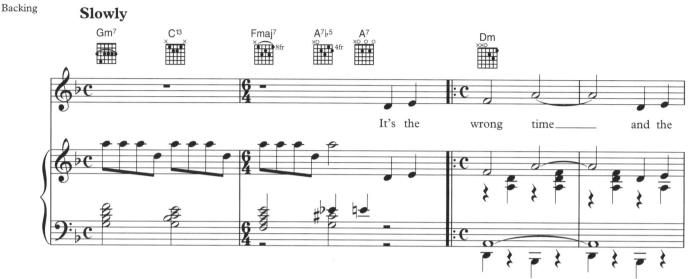

It's the wrong time____ and the

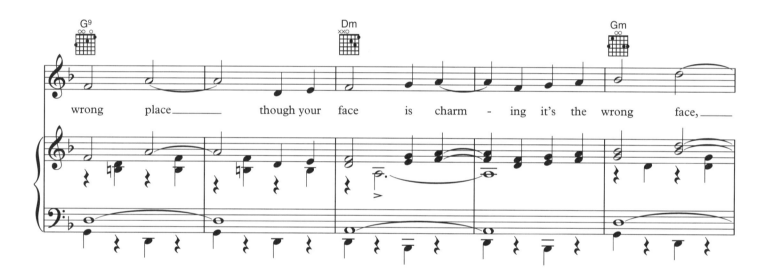

wrong place____ though your face is charm - ing it's the wrong face,____

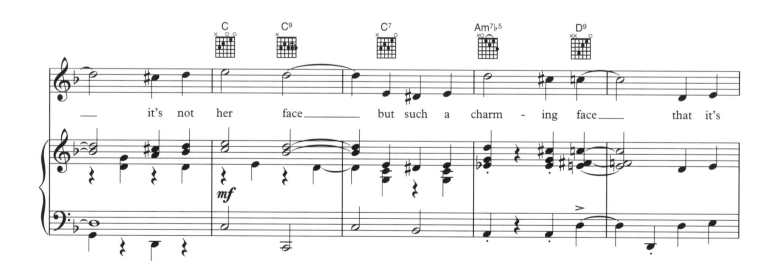

— it's not her face____ but such a charm - ing face____ that it's

lips are tempt - ing, they're the wrong lips,_____ they're not her lips,_____

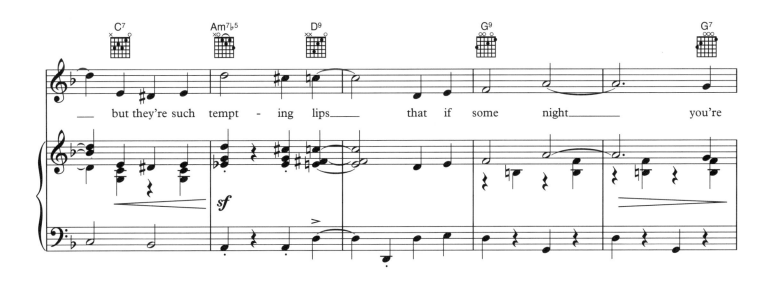

___ but they're such tempt - ing lips_____ that if some night_____ you're

free,_____ dear, it's al - right,_____ it's al - right_____

with me._____ It's the all right you bet-ter be-lieve it it's

all right___ yes it's all right___ with_____

me._____

I've Gotta Be Me

Words and Music by Walter Marks

Let's Face The Music And Dance

Words and Music by Irving Berlin

Backing

Moderately

There may be trou - ble a - head. _____

But while there's moon - light and mu - sic and love and ro -

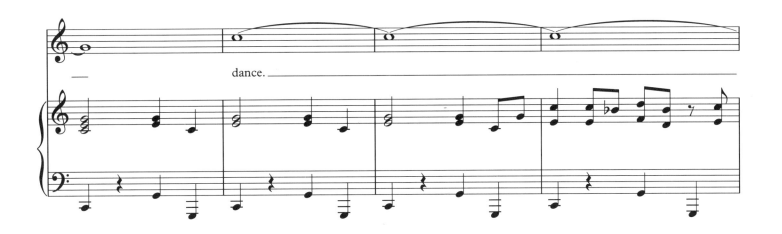

dance.

Love Me Or Leave Me

Words by Gus Kahn
Music by Walter Donaldson

Track 6
Backing

Love me or leave me, and let me be lone-ly. You won't be-lieve me, and

I love you on-ly; I'd rath-er be lone-ly than hap-py with some-bo-dy else.

I want your love, but I don't want to bor - row to haved it to - day, and to

give back to - mor - row, for my love is your love, there's no love for no - bo - dy else!

So_ love me or_ leave me now._

Mr Bojangles

Words and Music by Jerry Jeff Walker

(whistle)

1.I

knew a man,   Bo-jan-gles, and he'll__ dance   for   you, __
2. Told me of a time   he worked with,   with minstrel shows,
3. He said 'I dance   now and   every chance in honky tonks

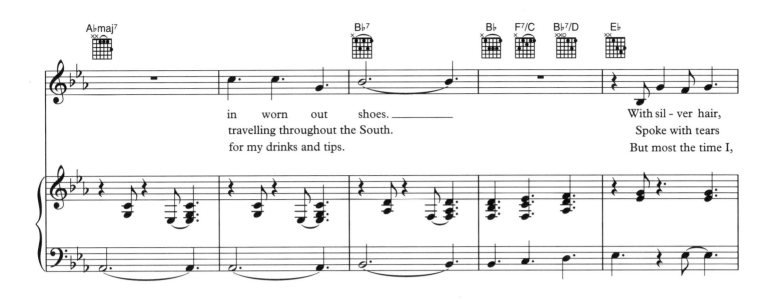

in worn out shoes. _____
travelling throughout the South.
for my drinks and tips.

With sil - ver hair,
Spoke with tears
But most the time I,

a rag - ged shirt,
for fifteen years
I spend behind these county bars,

bag - gy pants, _____
how his, how his dog and he,

he will do the old_____
they would travel
you see son, I

soft shoe. _____
about.
I drinks a bit'.

Come back and dance a - gain Mis - ter Bo - jan - gles__

(whistle)

September Song

Words by Maxwell Anderson
Music by Kurt Weill

Oh it's a long, long while from May to De - cem - ber, and the days grow short _____ when you reach Sep - tem - ber, _____ and the au - tumn

wea - ther turns the leaves to flame, and I have-n't got

time _____ for the wait - ing game. For the

days dwin-dle down _____ to a pre - cious few, _____ Sep-

tem - ber, No - vem - ber, and these few

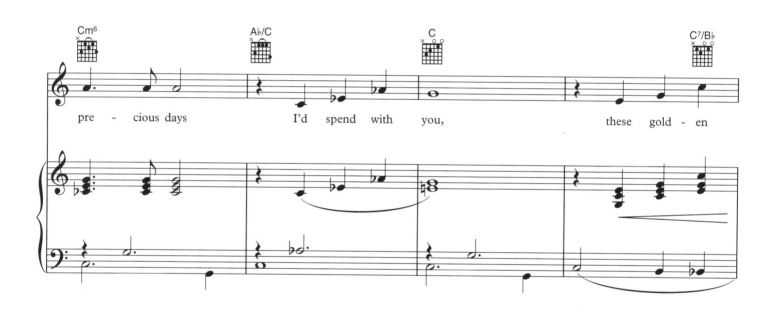

pre - cious days I'd spend with you, these gold - en

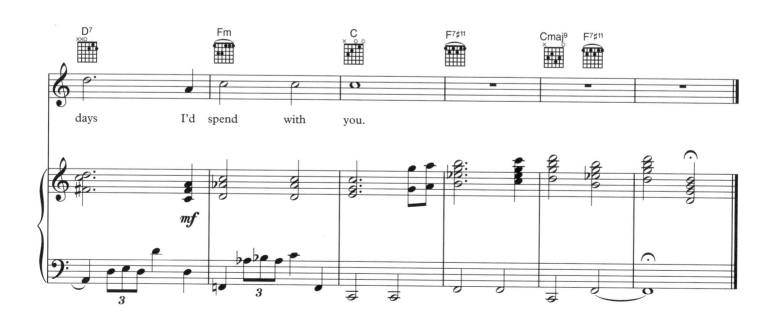

days I'd spend with you.

Something's Gotta Give

Words and Music by Johnny Mercer

Backing

Medium swing

When an ir - re - sist - i - ble force such as you

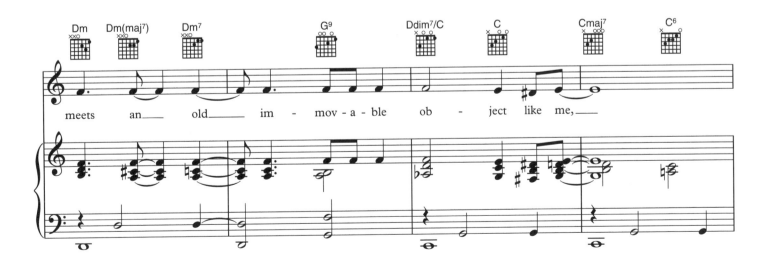

meets an old im - mov - a - ble ob - ject like me,

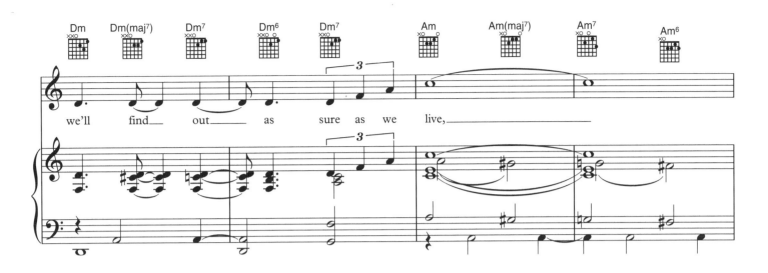

we'll find out as sure as we live,

1.

some-thing's got-ta give, some-thing's got-ta give, some-thing's got-ta give.

2.

some-thing, some-thing's got-ta give.

What Kind Of Fool Am I?

Words and Music by Leslie Bricusse and Anthony Newley

Backing

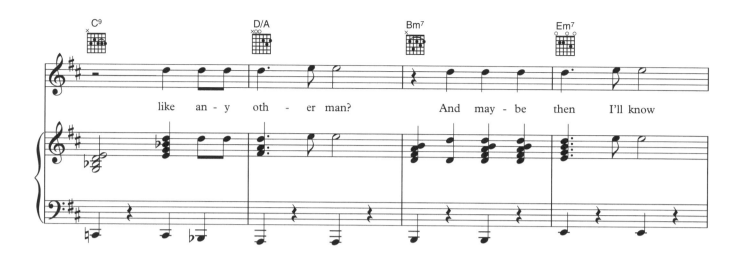

like an-y oth-er man? And may-be then I'll know

D.S. al Coda   Coda

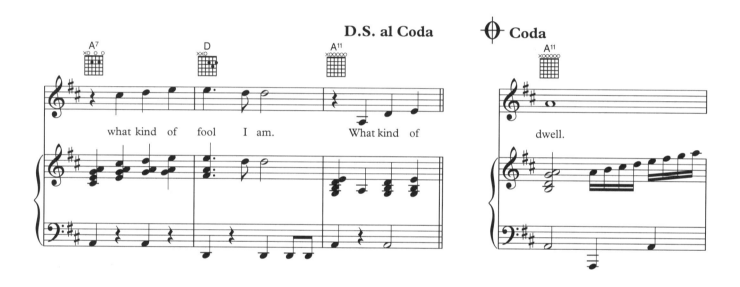

what kind of fool I am. What kind of

dwell.

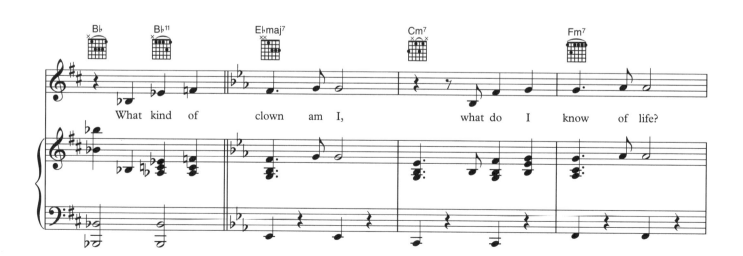

What kind of clown am I, what do I know of life?

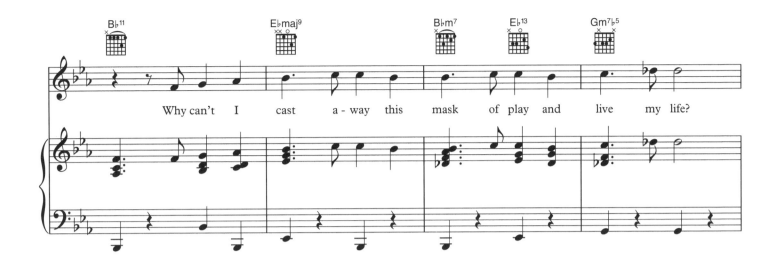

Why can't I cast a-way this mask of play and live my life?

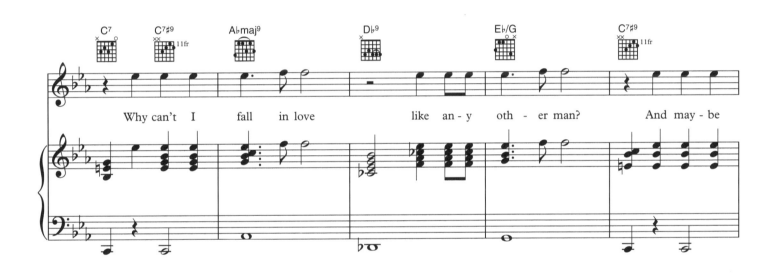

Why can't I fall in love like an-y oth-er man? And may-be

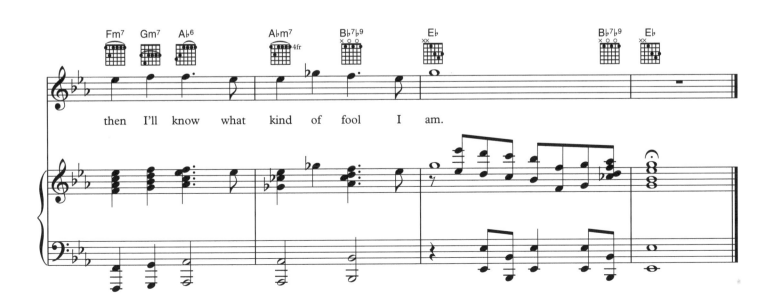

then I'll know what kind of fool I am.

YOU'RE THE VOICE

8861A PV/CD

Casta Diva from Norma – Vissi
D'arte from Tosca – Un Bel Di
Vedremo from Madama Butterfly –
Addio, Del Passato from La Traviata
– J'ai Perdu Mon Eurydice from
Orphee Et Eurydice – Les Tringles
Des Sistres Tintaient from Carmen
– Porgi Amor from Le Nozze Di
Figaro – Ave Maria from Otello

8860A PVG/CD

Delilah – Green Green Grass Of
Home – Help Yourself – I'll Never
Fall In Love Again – It's Not
Unusual – Mama Told Me Not To
Come – Sexbomb – Thunderball –
What's New Pussycat – You Can
Leave Your Hat On

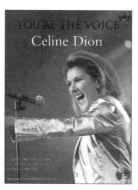

9297A PVG/CD

Beauty And The Beast – Because
You Loved Me – Falling Into You –
The First Time Ever I Saw Your
Face – It's All Coming Back To Me
Now – Misled – My Heart Will Go
On – The Power Of Love – Think
Twice – When I Fall In Love

9349A PVG/CD

Chain Of Fools – A Deeper Love
Do Right Woman, Do Right Man –
I Knew You Were Waiting (For Me)
– I Never Loved A Man (The Way I
Loved You) – I Say A Little Prayer –
Respect – Think – Who's Zooming
Who – (You Make Me Feel Like)
A Natural Woman

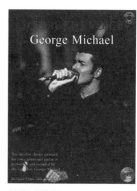

9007A PVG/CD

Careless Whisper – A Different
Corner – Faith – Father Figure –
Freedom '90 – I'm Your Man –
I Knew You Were Waiting (For Me)
– Jesus To A Child – Older –
Outside

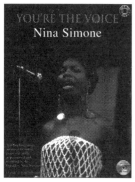

9606A PVG/CD

Don't Let Me Be Misunderstood –
Feeling Good – I Loves You Porgy –
I Put A Spell On You – Love Me Or
Leave Me – Mood Indigo – My Baby
Just Cares For Me – Ne Me Quitte
Pas (If You Go Away) – Nobody
Knows You When You're Down And
Out – Take Me To The Water

9700A PVG/CD

Beautiful – Crying In The Rain –
I Feel The Earth Move – It's Too
Late – (You Make Me Feel Like)
A Natural Woman – So Far Away –
Way Over Yonder – Where You
Lead – Will You Love Me
Tomorrow – You've Got A Friend

9746A PVG/CD

April In Paris – Come Rain Or
Come Shine – Fly Me To The Moon
(In Other Words) – I've Got You
Under My Skin – The Lady Is A
Tramp – My Kinda Town (Chicago
Is) – My Way – Theme From *New
York, New York* – Someone To
Watch Over Me – Something Stupid

9770A PVG/CD

Cry Me A River – Evergreen (A Star
Is Born) – Happy Days Are Here
Again – I've Dreamed Of You –
Memory – My Heart Belongs To Me
– On A Clear Day (You Can See
Forever) – Someday My Prince Will
Come – Tell Him (duet with Celine
Dion) – The Way We Were

9799A PVG/CD

Boogie Woogie Bugle Boy – Chapel
Of Love – Friends – From A
Distance – Hello In There – One
For My Baby (And One More For
The Road) – Only In Miami –
The Rose – When A Man Loves A
Woman – Wind Beneath My Wings

9810A PVG/CD

Ain't No Sunshine – Autumn Leaves
– How Can I Keep From Singing –
Imagine – It Doesn't Matter
Anymore – Over The Rainbow –
Penny To My Name – People Get
Ready – Wayfaring Stranger – What A
Wonderful World

9889A PVG/CD

Around The World – Born Free –
From Russia With Love – Gonna
Build A Mountain – The Impossible
Dream – My Kind Of Girl – On A
Clear Day You Can See Forever –
Portrait Of My Love – Softly As I
Leave You – Walk Away

10039A PVG/CD

All Of Me – Body And Soul – God
Bless The Child – I Love My Man
('Billie's Blues') – Lady Sings The
Blues – Lover Man (Oh Where Can
You Be) – The Man I Love – My
Man ('Mon Homme') – Night And
Day – St. Louis Blues

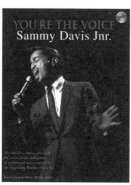

10091A PVG/CD

For Once In My Life – Hey There –
It's All Right With Me – I've Gotta
Be Me – Let's Face The Music And
Dance – Love Me Or Leave Me – Mr
Bojangles – September Song –
Something's Gotta Give – What
Kind Of Fool Am I?

10119A PVG/CD

Come Away With Me – Don't
Know Why – Don't Miss You At
All – Feelin' The Same Way –
Nightingale – Painter Song – The
Prettiest Thing – Sunrise – Those
Sweet Words – What Am I To You?

The outstanding vocal series from IMP

CD contains full backings for each song,
professionally arranged to recreate the sounds of the original recording